This Journal Belongs To:

_____

_____

_____

D1360501

breathe

Breathe Retreat, a one day, fully immersive and interactive
worship encounter for women.

Visit our website for upcoming retreats at breatheretreat.life

_____

_____

_____

_____

_____

_____

_____

_____

_____

_____

_____

_____

_____

_____

_____

_____

"The one who sows from a generous spirit will reap an abundant harvest." 2 Corinthians 9:6

_____

_____
_____
_____
_____
_____
_____
_____
_____
_____
_____
_____
_____
_____
_____
_____
_____
_____

*"And don't allow yourselves to be weary in
planting good seeds, for the season of reaping
the wonderful harvest you've planted is coming!"*
Galatians 6:9

"For you, Yahweh, always surround and protect me." Psalm 27:1

"Yahweh is my revelation—light and the source
of my salvation." Psalm 27:1

"I want to live with him every moment in his
house, beholding the marvelous beauty of
Yahweh." Psalms 27:4

"In the day of trouble, he will treasure me in his shelter, under the cover of his tent."
Psalms 27:5

"Yet I believe with all my heart that I will see again your goodness, Yahweh, in the land of life eternal!" Psalms 27:13

"Be brave and courageous, and never lose hope.
Yes, keep on waiting—for he will never
disappoint you!" Psalms 27:14

"Don't give up; don't be impatient; be entwined
as one with the Lord." Psalms 27:14

"Your visitations of glory bless the earth; the
rivers of God overflow and enrich it."
Psalms 65:9

"The harvest of the earth is here! God, the very God we worship, keeps us satisfied at his banquet of blessings." Psalms 67:6

"Bless us with a bountiful harvest, with golden grain swaying on the mountain fields! May the cities be full of praising people, fruitful and filled." Psalms 72:16

"Yes, the Lord keeps raining down blessing after blessing" Psalms 85:12

"They will return with joyful laughter and shouting with gladness as they bring back armloads of blessing and a harvest overflowing!" Psalms 126:6

"Those who sow their tears as seeds will reap a
harvest with joyful shouts of glee."
Psalms 126:5

Breathe is a 12-hour, fully interactive and immersive worship experience for women. It's a season of refreshing in an atmosphere of freedom and yieldedness to the breath of God. We will catch the wind of God and breathe the oxygen of heaven, as we press in and seek His face and His breakthrough.

It's time to be healed.
It's time to be restored.
It's time to breathe.

At the Breathe Retreat, there will be time and space set aside for intimate, Spirit-led worship, powerful ministry, inspired teachings, and workshops geared toward the lives, the struggles, and the victories that are common to every woman, young and old. God will have His way with us, and we will minister to Him and to each other!
-Sandy James, Founder of Breathe

Made in the USA
Coppell, TX
16 April 2022

76680404R00090